195195

underwater
and sea adventure

the story of the wonderful waters around the earth

under water

& sea adventure

by Patrick Ellam

A RUTLEDGE BOOK

GROSSET & DUNLAP · PUBLISHERS · NEW YORK

"*He goes a great
voyage that goes
to the bottom
of the sea*"

Thomas Fuller, 1732

contents

mighty waters | 1

Out in the middle, the wide oceans are just about the wildest places on earth. Swept by gales, hurricanes and tornadoes, the seas rage and thunder, while below the surface a never-ending battle goes on among fearsome marine creatures.

Someone figured that to equal the power of a hurricane you would have to drop an atom bomb every 15 minutes. That is 96 bombs a day. Since the average hurricane lasts for three or four days, you would need about 350 atom bombs to put on a show like one ordinary hurricane. A winter gale has about the same power; a tornado, or whirling windstorm accompanied by a funnel-shaped cloud, is smaller but fiercer while it lasts. Imagine living in a place where that sort of thing is going on all the time!

We were hit by a tornado in the Atlantic Ocean last year. We were sailing from Charleston, South Carolina, to the Virgin Islands in a 45-foot sailboat when, about 300 miles northeast of the Bahamas, we ran into a gale. Within 24

hours it had built up a big sea and we were lying to, sideways on to the waves, with just a tiny storm trysail up to steady the boat.

The wind was howling in the rigging, driving rain and spray across the decks, and the four of us aboard were in the cabin, holding on as the boat went up, up, up on a wave and then down into the trough between the seas, so fast that our feet lifted off the floor. Above the noise of the wind, we would hear an awful hissing sound. Quickly it would get louder and closer. A second of silence, then CRASH, as a wave broke over the boat, jerking her sideways a couple of feet, then rushing over the top of her, gurgling and spluttering as it went.

But she could take it. She was a new boat, and well built, and we had made all our preparations long before the storm arrived (as soon as the barometer had told me it was coming). The trysail was holding her fairly steady at an angle of about 30 degrees. The crew were all experienced deep-water sailors who had seen that sort of thing before,

Mountains of ice rise above water, but navigators know bergs hide their size below

and we were not unduly worried. Things were about normal for a small boat in a storm at sea.

Then one of the men, who was looking out of the hatch, came down and stood waiting to speak to me. I looked at him and cocked my head. He said, quite casually: "There's a funnel outside."

"A funnel?" I repeated. "Let's go and have a look at it." He went up ahead of me through the hatch and onto the deck. As I followed, the tornado struck us fair and square.

In an instant, the howling of the wind rose to an unearthly shriek, just like a jet plane taking off. The boat leaned over, ever so gently, until her mast was lying flat on the water, and at the same time she slid down, sideways, into the hollow of the waves. That saved us, for the worst of the wind was tearing by overhead from one wave top to the next and missing us, so that we only caught the edge of it.

The edge was quite enough. I have made a delayed jump by parachute and reached a speed in the air of around 115 miles an hour, but this wind was much faster than that. It was probably closer to 150 or 160 miles an hour.

My deck hand, who was a strong, heavy man, grabbed the steel lifeline just before the waterspout of the tornado struck, and he hung on for all he was worth. (The waterspout is a rapidly rotating column of wind going from a cloud to the surface of the ocean.) From the hatch I could see his whole body floating in the air, waving like a flag.

Then, as suddenly as it had come, the storm went by. The scream of the wind fell to a steady howl, the mast came up out of the water, and my deck hand fell back on deck. You would never believe how calm and peaceful and comforting it felt to be back in a plain, ordinary storm again.

Almost any part of the oceans can be wild at times, but some places are wild all the time. Cape Horn, at the southern tip of South America, is one. The wind howls round it at gale force for weeks at a time, with scarcely a letup, and the old sailing ships often used to take two or three weeks to fight their way round from one side of the Cape to the other.

Another truly wild place is the North Pole, which is in the Arctic Ocean. There you have not only howling gales but also bitter cold making it as fearsome a spot as you can imagine. And in the Arctic Ocean, icebergs and growlers break free and go drifting down into the North Atlantic to liven things up.

Icebergs come in all shapes and sizes, often several hundred yards long with great pinnacles rising 250 to 300 feet above the sea. Since ice is almost as heavy as water, the part under water that you can not see is seven or eight times as big as the part that shows.

Growlers are icebergs that have started melting and they are usually blue instead of white like an ordinary iceberg. They have great caves and holes in them and they often roll over in the water making the deep, growling noise that gives them their name.

the role of the tides

Have you ever wondered where the tide goes? All that water runs out to sea and comes back again all over the world, every day. Where does it go? And why?

The answer is fairly simple. The sun and the moon are at the bottom of it. The sun's gravity pulls the earth toward it, very hard indeed. That is what keeps the earth in orbit around the sun. Otherwise, it would go flying off into outer space and we'd all freeze solid. The moon's gravity is not so strong, but the moon is much closer to the earth, so that it too pulls at the earth very hard.

Now, the earth is so heavy and so solid that it just keeps on going, in a great curve around the sun, year after year. But the sea is free to move, and so it does.

Every day, as the earth spins around, the sun comes first over one ocean, then over another. And as it travels, it pulls the sea toward it, so that the whole ocean rises a little in the middle and pulls the water away from the sides. Then, as the sun passes by, the ocean goes down in the middle and out at the sides. That is what gives us our daily rise and fall of the tides.

Then the moon gets into the act. When it is nearly in line with the sun, both pull together, so that we get stronger tides that go both higher and lower than usual. These are called spring tides, and they happen every 28 days (that, by the moon, is one month). Then, when the moon rides at right angles to the sun, we get weaker tides, called neap tides, that do not go so high or low as spring tides.

To make things more tricky, the moon rushes around the earth in a curious pattern and the sea gets pulled sideways, as well as upwards, by both sun and moon as they go by. The water, being heavy, is slow to follow all this and lags behind. Therefore, figuring out the time high tide will be next year is very hard indeed. In fact, the tide tables that you can buy, which give the times of high water in various ports for a year ahead, are worked out by seeing at what hours the tides were high over several years past and working forward from there, because nobody has yet figured out how to do it any other way.

Apart from spring and neap tides, the heights of the tides vary a great deal from place to place. In Norway they vary as little as nine inches from high to low at springs, and only four inches at neaps. Yet in the Bay of Fundy, in Nova Scotia, they sometimes run as high as 70 feet at springs.

Along our coasts, the tides run from three to ten feet, from high to low, while in Europe they usually vary a little more than that. But here and there you run into a specially high one.

The first time I took a sailboat into Boulogne harbor, in France, it was just high water. When we had anchored the boat and rowed over to shore in the little dinghy, the top of the dock stood about two feet out of the water. I had heard that they had very high tides there, but I had not bothered to look up the exact height in the tide tables. So, to be on the safe side, I tied up the dinghy with a rope 20 feet long. Then we went ashore for lunch and wandered around the town, doing some shopping.

About three hours later, when we came back, we found the dinghy hanging by its rope, easily ten feet clear above the water. The tide had gone down 40 feet, and we had to wait on the dock for it to come back before we could get our dinghy.

the power of the tides

Water is quite heavy. A tank six feet square and six feet high would hold over six tons of it. One really big wave weighs thousands of tons, so the total weight of water that goes up and down each day on the tides must be enormous.

Every now and then you hear of some

Heeled over against heavy swell, these fishermen agree oceans are wildest places on earth

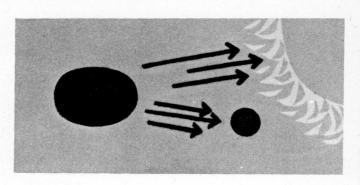

Spring tides are high because at these times the moon and sun pull roughly in same direction, giving maximum difference between flood and ebb

scheme to harness the tides and use their power. If we could do this on a big scale, we would get—for free—all the power we could possibly use. But nobody has managed to do this yet.

Usually the tide goes up and down so slowly that you can hardly see it move. But there are a few places where it comes in with a rush. The River Seine, in France, is one. There, due to the shape of the sandy bottom, the tide comes roaring in, in three great waves, one after the other. This is called a bore. There is another one in Nova Scotia, and another of the same kind in China.

A friend of ours was sailing up the Seine in a 30-foot sailboat a few years ago. He had anchored off a village for the night and was making his supper when he heard a noise on the shore. A group of people on the bank stood shouting and waving at him. But he didn't speak French so he could not understand what they were saying.

Then, in the distance, he heard a low rumble. Steadily it grew louder and louder until, around a bend in the river, a great wave appeared and came rushing up the river toward him, hissing and roaring. Before he could do a thing, the wave took hold of the boat, spinning it round and throwing his supper all over the cabin. Then came a second wave, and a third.

His boat bobbed like a cork, but she was a seagoing vessel and survived all right. Even so, after the third wave had passed, she was left swinging to and fro across the river on her anchor, for the tide was rushing up the river as fast as it could go. After maybe half an hour, the fuss died down, and he cleaned up the mess and cooked himself a fresh supper. But he didn't try anchoring in that part of the Seine again.

what are tidal waves?

Sometimes you hear of tidal waves that do tremendous damage, especially in the Pacific Ocean. But actually they have nothing to do with the tide. They are either storm waves or tsunamis (pronounced tsoo-nan-me).

A storm wave is caused by a big storm, such as a hurricane, and happens in three ways. First, the wind drives the ocean currents faster than usual and they come together at the shore with nowhere to go. Second, a very strong wind will actually pile the water up on top of itself at the surface. And third, the low pressure in the air during a storm causes the water level to rise.

Sometimes all three things happen at once, and then you get storm waves as high as 20 feet breaking along the shore, tearing down buildings, sinking boats and killing people. About three-quarters of all the people who have been killed by hurricanes were killed by the storm

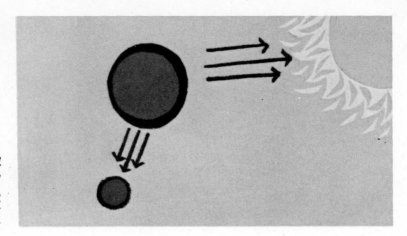

During neap *tides, sun and moon tug at waters in nearly opposite directions. Thus, the difference between flood and ebb is at its minimum*

waves they made.

A tsunami is quite different and usually much worse, though less frequent. Tsunamis are caused by earthquakes, by volcanoes erupting, or by big landslides along the coast. In whichever case, the sudden shock sends a series of waves that travel for thousands of miles at very high speed across the surface of the ocean.

In deep water, most waves are two or three feet high, and so long (more than 100 miles from one crest to the next) that you cannot even see them. In fact, it may take up to an hour for one wave to go past you, so it goes up and down very slowly indeed.

But the tsunamis travel at over 400 knots and have tremendous energy locked up in them. There are from five to 15 of them, with the biggest one in the middle and smaller ones on either side. And when they get into the shallow water near a coast, the trouble starts. Suddenly they pile up into great breakers weighing thousands of tons each that go thundering up the shore, knocking everything flat as they go.

One tsunami started off the Aleutian Islands on April 1, 1946. Four and a half hours later it hit Hawaii, over 2,200 miles away, with waves 50 feet high that killed 173 people and did $25,000,000 worth of damage. Hawaii gets one of those only once every 20 years but that is quite enough.

the currents

Some people call currents tides, but that is not exact. Tides go up and down, while currents move to and fro. Many currents are caused by tides, but there are also currents caused by wind, or by great rivers, or by the different levels of two bodies of water. The most important currents are caused by wind.

All around the earth, for about 1,000 miles on each side of the equator, the northeast and southeast trade winds blow strong and steady, year after year. These are called equatorial currents, and as they sweep across the great oceans, they push the water along, sending vast, slow-moving currents from one continent to another.

The Atlantic Ocean is typical. There the equatorial current runs from Africa to the northeastern corner of South America, where it splits in halves. One half goes southward, while the other half swings up northward through the gaps between the Windward Islands and

17

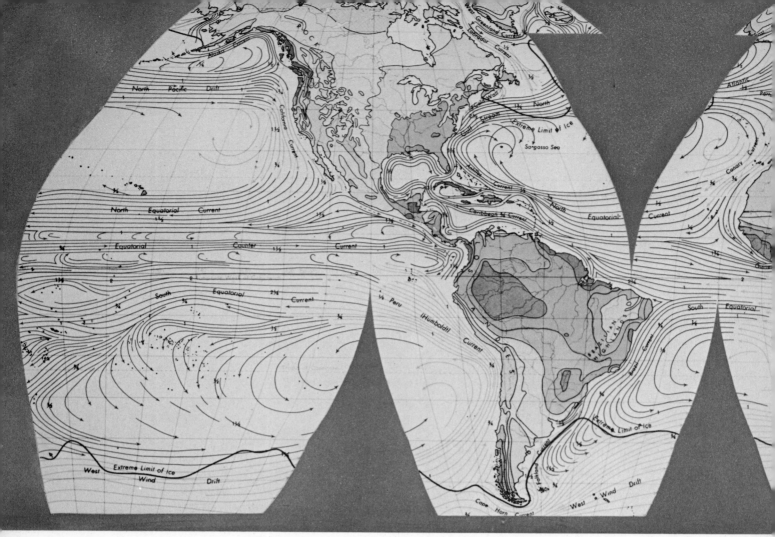

This map gives location and direction of the ocean currents. Note circular movements

into the Caribbean Sea. It runs through here, at about one knot, on up into the Gulf of Mexico where it finds it can't go any farther. So it swings around and goes through the Straits of Florida, between Florida and Cuba, then north between Florida and the Bahamas.

But the Straits of Florida are only about 40 miles wide, so the water has to speed up, to keep ahead of the wide stream behind it. Up goes the speed to four knots.

That doesn't sound like much until you realize the amount of water we are talking about. Twenty-five million tons of water pass through the Straits of Flori-

da every second of the day, every day of the year. While you were reading that last sentence, another hundred million tons or so went through. That's a great deal of water.

It comes surging out of the Straits in a steady stream, called the Gulf Stream, with so much weight behind it that it merges with the North Atlantic Drift Current, goes across the Atlantic Ocean, past England and up along the coast of Norway, well over 5,000 miles away.

As it flows it slows down, but it picks up water on either side of it and carries that along with it, so that it passes New York at the rate of 50 million tons a sec-

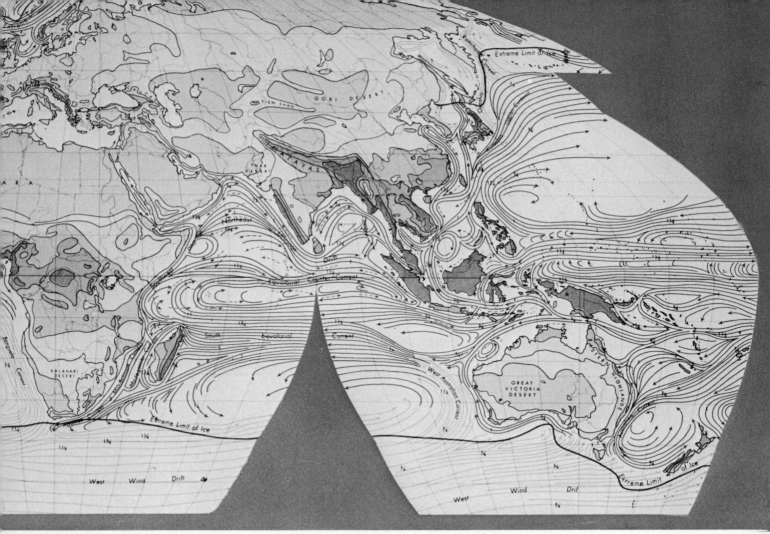

within major areas, ice limits, and wind drifts. Map copyright by Rand McNally, 60Y61

ond. Twice as much water as in the Straits of Florida!

Now, the surface water of the Gulf Stream is in the tropics for nearly six months, on its way from Africa to Florida, and by the time it reaches Florida its temperature is about 82 degrees, which is very warm. Also, the current is so big that the water cools very slowly and is still quite warm when it reaches England.

There the southwest winds carry the heat over the land, which is why England is much warmer than France in winter.

About half the sea water in the world stays between 70 and 85 degrees near the surface, all the year round, and nearly a quarter of it stays between 80 and 85 degrees. But deeper down it cools off quite rapidly until, in the Pacific Ocean, all the water below 540 fathoms is almost cold enough to freeze.

The other kind of currents, which are due to the different levels of two bodies of water, are called hydraulic currents. A typical one is Barnegat Bay, in New Jersey. There you have a long, land-locked lake, connected to the sea by a narrow canal at Manasquan Inlet. Whenever the sea level is higher than the level of the lake, the current runs in through the canal, and when the levels are reversed, it runs out.

This current, then, does not turn when the tide turns but when the levels are equal, or about three hours later. And it turns very suddenly. I have stood on a bridge there and watched a piece of straw in the water coming rapidly toward me. Then suddenly, with hardly a pause, it has stopped and floated off the other way.

Around our coasts, the currents flow mostly at from one to three knots, but there are places where they go up to six knots (such as Hell Gate, in New York City). And I know of one place, off the coast of France, where the current gets up to ten knots at springs. It is called the Chenal de Four, a narrow, twisting channel between Ushant Island and the mainland, near the port of Brest. It has rocks on either side, and the current runs through it so fast that the stone lighthouses marking the channel seem to rush at you, leaving foaming wakes like destroyers. I once took a sailboat with no engine through there, and it wasn't exactly a peaceful trip.

When you are out at sea, you often come across a place where two currents meet. On a calm day, there will be a long, wavy line of seaweed, maybe a yard wide and stretching as far as you can see. And you can clearly tell that on one side of the line the water is flowing

Roaring in across the ocean comes the dangerous waterspout, a sky-high tube of whirling wind, mist and water spray

A tsunami, a great sea wave that may travel for thousands of miles, is produced by volcanoes or earth movements under water

past the weed. In fact, in a small sailboat, it pays you to move over into the more favorable current and let it push you along.

Caught among the weeds will be old crates, bottles and scraps of wood. And in among them you will find cuttlefish. Those are white fossils, oval-shaped and about six by two inches, that are fine for rubbing down brightwork before you varnish it. So you steer wildly down the line for a while, swerving from side to side, with a man leaning over each side, grabbing cuttlefish as you go by.

water and weather

The sea has quite an effect on the weather. For one thing, it heats up and cools down much more slowly than the land. So in the day time the land gets hotter than the water, and by night it gets cooler. In either case, the air over the warmer body rises and lets the cooler air rush in to take its place. This gives us our cool onshore breezes in the daytime and our offshore breezes at night.

Early one morning, two of us were sailing along in a 20-foot open boat about 25 miles off the coast of Ceylon, in the Indian Ocean. My friend was asleep on the floor and I was steering, feeling tired after an all-night sail.

Then, suddenly I noticed ahead of us a man sitting in an ordinary kitchen chair on the water, fishing. I couldn't see any boat, so I called my friend to have a look. He saw the same thing. Maybe I wasn't going mad after all. We sailed over to see what was going on.

The man was on a jaganda. This is a crude native raft made of half a dozen logs tied together, side by side. This jaganda was about 16 feet long by 5 feet wide, and the logs were awash so that you couldn't see them until you were very close. Obviously, it was far too heavy for one man to paddle, and we wondered how he would get back to land.

Then we saw that he had a mast and a sail lying on the logs, so he could sail—but only down wind, for that thing would never go to windward. We soon found the answer. He must leave before dawn and sail out to sea on the last of the offshore breeze. Then he takes down his sail and fishes, drifting around in deep water. In the afternoon, he puts up his sail and lets the onshore breeze carry him home. But what happened to him if the onshore breeze didn't come we never found out. Probably he would have to drift around, eating raw fish and hoping that it would come the next day.

Another way the sea affects the weather is by its warm and cool currents. When you sail into the Gulf Stream, you know it. There are nearly always fierce little squalls all over the

21

Like a big vacuum cleaner, a tornado's funnel races over the sea sucking up everything in its way

The average hurricane, smashing across sea and land, packs the power of 350 atom bombs

place, and you have to keep a sharp eye out for them until you are clear of the Gulf Stream.

But it is a wonderful place to catch sailfish and marlin and other big game fish that feed in its warm waters. For the same reason, it is not a good place to go swimming, because of the sharks.

If you catch a shark, cut out its liver and throw the rest away (unless you like shark's fin soup, which isn't bad). Then cut up the liver and leave it on a sloping roof in the sun. Slowly the oil will seep out of it, and you catch that with a funnel, as it drips off the roof, and put it in small bottles. This oil has an almost magical property.

I have a bottle of shark's liver oil on my desk now. The bottom quarter of an inch looks white and hard, and I can't see through it. But above that all the rest is as clear as water. This means that it will be a fine day tomorrow. If it were going to be a bad day, the oil would be white and cloudy, like milk, right up to the top.

This is an old seaman's gadget, and it works about as well as anything else for telling the weather. But the odd thing is that the bottle is firmly corked, with a screw cap on top of that. How it works its magic I don't know.

the ocean floor | 2

Nearly three-quarters of the earth is covered with water. You could fit all the land into the Pacific Ocean alone, with plenty of room to spare. The oceans are about four times as deep as the land is high, so that the land mass would sink without a trace. The Atlantic Ocean is about 12 times as big as the United States, and the Pacific is twice as big as the Atlantic. Yet until some 90 years ago we had only the slightest idea of what went on in the great oceans, and even today we don't know very much. We know about the surface, but the vast world below has yet to be explored.

Since we cannot see deep down into the water, the only way to find out the shape of the bottom is to take soundings (that is, to measure the depth at different points) until we have enough information to make a map. For thousands of years, men have been taking soundings in shallow waters, although more than 2,000 years ago someone actually found a place 6,000 feet deep near Sardinia. Until recently the only way to do it was to lower a weight to the bottom, and in

deep water this method took several hours to complete one sounding.

Then, in 1922, the echo sounder came along. This is a machine that makes a loud "ping" under the water. The sound goes down to the bottom and is reflected back up, just as an echo comes back if you shout in a deep cave. When it gets back, the machine measures how long it took for the round trip. And since the speed of sound in sea water is about 4,945 feet a second (or four and a half times as fast as it travels in air), the machine can easily figure how deep the water is.

With an echo sounder, a ship can sail along at full speed, taking soundings all the way. In one run, say from New York to Gibraltar, she can get a continual line of soundings across the Atlantic Ocean. By doing that thousands of times, along different lines, we can slowly build up a chart of the ocean floor.

A chart is a map of the sea, with soundings all over it, that tells a navigator where he can safely take his ship. The soundings are marked in fathoms

Skin diver descends, wearing cold-water suit with depth gauge on his wrist. He carries his camera

and show as numbers on the chart.

A fathom is six feet (or two yards) and is the length of rope that a man can measure off by stretching his arms sideways. 1,000 fathoms (or 2,000 yards) are one nautical mile. That is a nice round number and happens to be the same as one minute of latitude, which makes navigation much easier than it would be with ordinary miles, which are 1,760 yards long and don't match anything.

Then, for speeds at sea we use knots. One knot is one nautical mile per hour. Sometimes you hear people talking about "Knots per hour" but that is repetitive nonsense.

Anyway, once echo sounders came along we began to get a much better idea of the shape of the ocean floor. We found that along the coasts of the continents the bottom gradually slopes to about 100 fathoms and then suddenly falls steeply away into much deeper water, forming a sort of flat shelf.

These are called continental shelves. They are usually about 30 miles wide, though they may be anything from 800 miles wide (off the Arctic coast of Siberia) down to almost nothing. Sometimes you find the same kind of shelf around an island, and that is called an insular shelf. In time we discovered that these shelves are not all so flat. They are covered with rolling hills, ridges, terraces and great canyons (the largest are

Off Puerto Rico a piston corer was lowered to cut out samples of the ocean's floor

as big as the Grand Canyon in Arizona).

One night, four of us were sailing toward New York in a 53-foot sailboat out of Bermuda. I figured we were about 100 miles from the shore, and I had gone sound asleep in my bunk when the man on watch called down the hatch: "Hey, Skipper! Come and look at this."

I went up on deck, rubbed the sleep out of my eyes, and looked around. The boat was heeling to a nice breeze and slicing silently along at about six knots. The night was as black as the inside of a cow. And there, ahead of us, lying low on the water, was a whole string of white lights, looking exactly like a small village.

I took a sounding but got no bottom (our little echo sounder went down only

In his bathysphere, Dr. William Beebe has gone deep into the ocean and brought back new facts about life under the water

The Cetacean is a deep-diving submarine equipped with four huge lights for undersea exploration

20 fathoms). So I told the man on watch to stay on his course, and I went up onto the foredeck to keep a lookout. As we got closer, I saw what it was—a fleet of fishing boats over the Hudson Canyon, each with its white deck lights on and men at work on deck, gutting and cleaning the fish as they were caught.

For thousands of years, the cold water from the Hudson River has been running across the continental shelf off New York until it has cut a deep canyon that is a great feeding place for fish. The next morning, as it grew light, we saw that the water was green instead of the deep blue of the ocean. We were over the shelf.

When you cross the edge of the shelf, going out to seaward, you find that the bottom drops quite suddenly from 100 fathoms to 2,000. That is quite a drop. From 600 feet down to 12,000 feet. Then you are really over the ocean floor.

the mountain ranges beneath the sea

If you look at a chart of the Atlantic Ocean, you will see that there is a great underwater mountain range, called the Atlantic Ridge, that runs all the way from Iceland down as far as the bottom tip of South America, with only one break in it (the Romanche Furrow, near the equator). Here and there, the ridge sticks up out of the water, to form an island. The Azores, St. Paul, Ascension and St. Helena are all peaks of the Atlantic Ridge that just happen to be high enough to show above the

Ancient treasures, like these vases, lie waiting on ocean floor for explorers to find them

29

Diagram shows how an echo sounder works. Machine measures time needed for sound to travel to bottom and back, thus determining depth

water (that is, over 12,000 feet high).

Then there are other ridges that run east and west, as far as the continents on either side, leaving a series of huge oval basins along both sides of the Atlantic Ridge. And, dotted around, you will find smaller, flat-topped underwater mountains (called the Guyots). Many of these have only been discovered quite recently, and there are probably quite a few more that haven't been found yet.

The Pacific Ocean is much the same, except that it is twice as big and slightly deeper. There again, many of the islands are in fact the tops of underwater mountains that stick up out of the sea, and between the mountain ranges you have vast, deep, oval-shaped basins.

Then there is the Indian Ocean, slightly smaller than the Atlantic, and lastly the Arctic Ocean, which is about half as big as that. The Indian Ocean is much the same as the Atlantic and the Pacific, but the Arctic Ocean is largely covered with ice, so that we still know very little about it.

The U. S. atomic submarine "Nautilus" (see p. 80) took soundings when she crossed the ocean (under the North Pole) recently, but they only gave us one thin line of depths, and it will probably be a long time before we really know what goes on up there. The Arctic Ocean covers about five and a half million square miles, quite a bit to explore.

In addition to the huge ocean basins, there are some spots that are very deep indeed. The deepest is the Marianas Trench in the Pacific, which goes down to 35,640 feet (the highest mountain in the world, Mount Everest, is only 29,002 feet high), and the deepest place in the Atlantic is the Puerto Rico Trough (28,-800 feet).

I have passed over the Puerto Rico Trough four times in small sailboats, but I have never noticed anything unusual. Once you get off the shelf, into water a couple of thousand fathoms deep, it all feels and looks much the same on the surface.

But sometimes, when you are alone on watch on a dark night, with the wind sighing in the rigging, you do wonder just what lives down there. Sea water has all the chemicals needed to support life, and the oceans have about 300 times as much space for things to live as has the land. So you sit. And you wonder. And you wait for the next man to come on watch. And you hope that nothing very big will stick its head out of the sea.

from the ocean depths

There is one strange thing that happens all over the deep oceans. Quite often you will get a strong ping on the echo sounder, from a depth of about 200 fathoms during the day, or slightly closer to the surface at night. This is

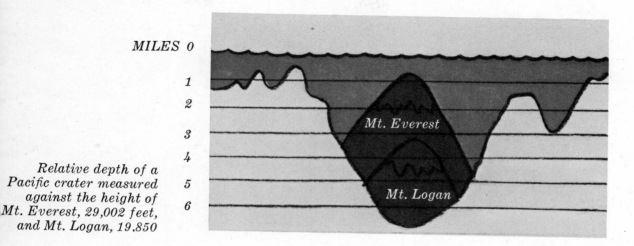

Relative depth of a Pacific crater measured against the height of Mt. Everest, 29,002 feet, and Mt. Logan, 19.850

called the phantom bottom, and we think that it is caused by thousands of tiny marine animals, though nobody is quite sure. But we do know that a big school of fish will give an echo that you can spot easily, and fishing fleets use echo sounders for just that purpose.

Another strange thing that happens, though not so often, is that an island will suddenly appear out of the sea. This is usually caused by a volcano erupting. Sometimes they will be good, solid islands that stay put, but others come up for a while and then disappear under the sea again.

One island came up in the middle of the Mediterranean Sea, between Sicily and Africa, in 1831. The water there was 100 fathoms deep until, one day, a volcano appeared out of nowhere and threw up a great pile of ash that rose 200 feet out of the sea.

The Italians promptly named it Isola Ferdinandia. The French decided to call it Ile Julie, and the English named it

Graham's Island. Then, three months later, it went back under the sea. So the Italians and the French withdrew their claims and left the English stuck with Graham's Reef.

But many islands that we know today were formed in the same way. Christmas Island, in the Indian Ocean, is one, and there are dozens of others in the Pacific Ocean. Mount Vesuvius began as a submarine volcano in a bay in the Mediterranean, and so did Mount Etna, which is 10,758 feet high today.

Apart from islands that are really mountain tops and those that are the tops of underwater volcanoes, there are coral islands. These are formed by millions of tiny marine plants and animals that leave little pieces of limestone behind them (the shell of a sea anemone is made of the same stuff).

This happens where there is already a platform near the surface for them to build on—either a big guyot or an old, dead underwater volcano. Bermuda is

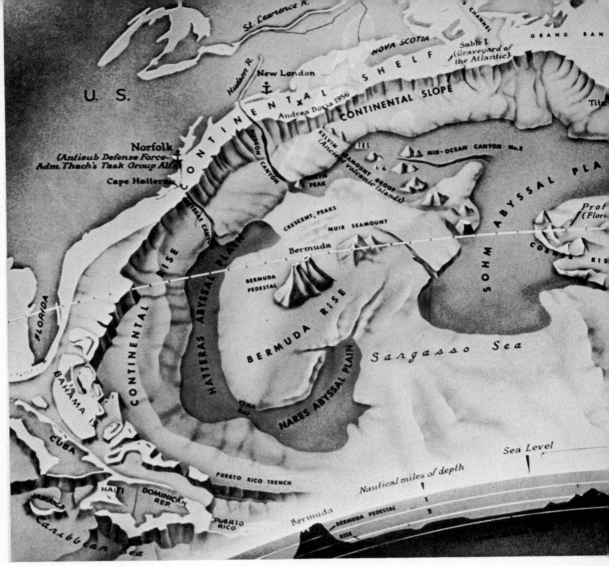

This map shows continental shelves, slopes and plains on Atlantic Ocean's floor from U.S.

an example. If you buy a piece of land there and start to build a house, you find that about a foot down the ground is solid limestone.

That is fine stuff for building with. It is so soft that you can cut it with a wood saw, but after you have built your house of it, it hardens in the weather until, a few years later, you have a good, solid house (though you have to varnish it on the windward side to stop the rain from washing it away before it has time to harden).

And, lastly, there are islands made of sand or rock or soil, and which are sim-

ply places where the sea is so shallow that the bottom sticks out of the water. Many of the small islands around our coasts are this kind.

the oceans vary

The sea itself varies quite a bit from place to place. For days the water will be deep blue and very clear and will feel warm. Then, one day, you notice that it feels cold. That means that you have crossed over the Gulf Stream into the colder water toward the American coast. And the next day it will be green and not so clear, which means that you are

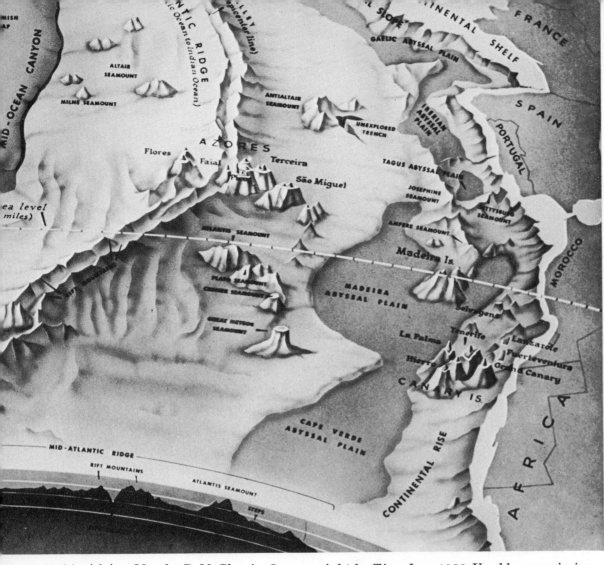

coast to Africa. Map by R. M. Chapin, Jr. copyright by Time Inc., 1958. Used by permission

in shallower water, over the continental shelf. When that happens, you start cleaning up the boat to be ready for your arrival in port, for you know you have less than 100 miles to go.

All over the great oceans, the salinity (or saltiness) of the water is generally about the same. The salt varies between 33 and 37 parts in 1,000, although you can't tell the difference by the taste of it. But in some places, such as the Dead Sea, it is much saltier, while there are a few places where it is quite fresh. Here great rivers run into the ocean, sending vast amounts of fresh water far out in-

to the sea.

There was one man who was sailing, all alone, in a small boat along the coast of South America. He had been becalmed for days and he was getting very worried that he might run out of fresh water and die. He was only 20 miles offshore, but with no wind and no motor he couldn't reach land.

Then he saw a ship, so he signalled it and asked for some water. The ship promptly signalled back: "Put a bucket over the side." He did, and he found that he was floating in millions of gallons of perfectly good, fresh water. He was off

The water boils (above) as an underwater volcano spits up new island which may last or disappear beneath waves, unlike coral reefs (below) which do last since they're built up by tiny animals, each adding a dot of limestone

34

the mouth of the Amazon.

Apart from the taste of it, salt water is a good deal heavier than fresh water, by about a pound and a half for every cubic foot. This makes quite a difference to ships, for they float deeper in fresh water than they do in salt. A captain bound for the Great Lakes (where the water is fresh) with a full cargo has to be careful that he doesn't find his ship overloaded when he gets there.

Another thing that varies from place to place in the sea is the transparency (or clearness) of the water. There is a way of measuring that. You take a round white disk, just under a foot across (30 centimeters, to be exact), called a Secchi disk, and you lower it into the water on a line until you can't see it any more. Then you measure how far down it was when it disappeared. The farther down you can see it, the clearer the water is.

Around the coast, you can see the disk anywhere from 15 to 80 feet down, but out in the deep oceans you can still see it at 150 to 200 feet, and once someone got a measurement of 217 feet in the Sargasso Sea, where the water is very clear indeed. But close inshore, where the water is often full of stirred-up sand and mud, you can sometimes see it for only a few feet.

Far from land, the ocean is deep blue. This is because the sunlight is scattered by tiny particles in the water. Blue light is more scattered than other colors (due to its short wave length) so the water looks blue. The sky looks blue for the same reason, except that in this case particles in the air do the scattering.

But in shallow water the blue is mixed with yellow (caused by tiny shrimplike creatures called plankton) so that it looks green. And in some places it looks brown or red, due to algae (the slimy stuff that forms in swimming pools) in the water.

Everywhere it gets darker quite rapidly as you go down deeper. It is not easy to see that for yourself, because of the pressure of the water above you. At 30 feet down, the pressure is twice what you are used to on land. At 60 feet, it is three times as much, and so on. At 300 feet, the pressure is about 11 times normal (the most a human being can stand, even for a short time).

If you built a very strong submarine and went down to 1,000 fathoms, the pressure would be 2,680 pounds on every square inch of the hull. And at 5,000 fathoms it would be 13,520 pounds per square inch. That is about six and three-quarter tons. So, a window a foot square would have on it a pressure of just under 1,000 tons, and the pressure on the whole hull would be truly enormous. It has been done, as we shall see, but it is quite a trick.

going below | 3

One day about five years ago, four of us were sailing up the Windward Islands, between South America and Puerto Rico, in a 40-foot sailboat. The northeast Trade Wind was humming in our rigging and the deep blue waters of the Caribbean Sea were churning into white foam under our bow as we approached the Tobago Gays, five tiny islands far from civilization.

Carefully we picked our way between the breakers that marked the reefs and into the still waters of the lagoon, to drop our anchor between two of the islands. The water there was pale green and so clear that we could see our anchor twenty feet below us lying on the sandy bottom. We had all the equipment we needed aboard the boat, so we decided to try skin diving.

First we tried the swimming fins, or 'flippers', on our feet. They felt strange at first but we soon found that a slow, easy motion—rather like pedalling a bicycle—would send us slicing through the water with very little effort, leaving our hands free for other things.

Then we put on the rubber face masks that go over your eyes and nose. You have to get the straps tight on these, or the water gets inside and goes up your nose. Also you will find that the glass window soon gets steamed up so that you can't see anything. If you cut a potato in half and rub it over the glass, it leaves a film of oil behind that prevents that from happening.

Finally we tried the breathing tubes (called 'snorkels' after the ones fitted to German submarines). They go from your mouth round to the back of your head, so that you can swim with your face under water and still breathe. They have a ball in a cage at the top, arranged so that as you dive it rises and blocks the tube, preventing the water from coming in. This works well, but it takes a while to get used to breathing in through the tube and out through your nose.

Equipped like this, we climbed down into the water, swam clear of the boat, and put our faces under the surface. Suddenly we found ourselves in a complete-

37

A small fish seeks protection between brain coral and sea rose

ly different world. Everything we were used to had gone. No land, no trees, no sun, no wind. No noise at all, just an eerie silence. In place of air there was water, pale green and hazy, like a heavy mist, so that we could see for perhaps forty feet and that was all.

We could see the bottom part of the boat, under the water, but not the top. Below us was the sandy bottom, with strange creatures on it. Above us, the surface of the water shimmered like a huge golden-green mirror, shining bright in the sun above. But we couldn't see through it. And all around us small fish, as big as your hand and all different in color, swam by minding their own business.

I had often wondered what a fish could see. The answer is that in very clear water he can see about forty feet around him and below him but upwards he can only see clearly as far as the surface. Directly overhead he has a round patch, some three feet across, where he can see things above the water, but they are distorted by the ripples at the surface and not very clear, like looking

through rippled glass. The rest of the surface acts like a big, shiny roof reflecting the rocks and things on the bottom, mingled with sunlight filtering down from above.

Our first reaction to it all was to run out of breath: It just doesn't seem right to breathe in with your face under water, and your natural inclination is to come up for air. But after a few tries, we got used to breathing through the snorkel and could start cruising farther afield.

Swimming along on the surface with your face under water is rather like flying in an airplane. The bottom rolls slowly by below you, with patches of white sand and patches of brown rock, with dark green weeds on them like long grasses.

When you want to go down and look at something, you take a deep breath, hold it, put your head down, paddle with your feet and down you go in a sweeping dive. You can skim along a few inches over the bottom or level-off at any height you please.

Most people can hold their breath for about a minute, then they have to come

This skin diver wears flippers and an air mask that lets him stay below for a half hour

up for air. So we soon got in the habit of cruising along on the surface, breathing through the snorkel, until we saw something interesting, when we would dive down to look at it.

Going up or down is just as easy as turning left or right. In fact we tried putting our arms straight out sideways and doing 'loops' and 'rolls' just like an airplane, using our hands as ailerons (the control surface at the ends of the wings). It is fun and it gives you confidence in what you can do.

the common creatures

The strange creatures we had seen on the bottom at the start turned out to be sea eggs. There are two kinds of those: Black and white. The white ones are round and hard, a bit smaller than a baseball, with spikes about two inches long all over them. They move around at about the same speed as a snail and their spikes are soft and brittle, so that they are quite harmless. You can eat them, raw or cooked, though they are rather tasteless and unappetizing.

39

*Black sea eggs, with their nine-inch-long
spines, can stab deeply into a man's skin*

But the black ones need watching.
They are jet black and shiny, with a
body almost as big as a softball covered
with hard spikes fully nine inches long.
If you brush against one, the spikes go
into your flesh and break off level with
the skin so that you can't get them out.
This is very painful, though not actually
dangerous.

As we moved over towards the reef,
we came across coral 'heads' in the sand,
hunks of white coral sticking straight
up, some as small as a human head and
some as large as a boulder. They were
firmly anchored and felt rough to the
touch, like soft rock.

Often there would be sea fans attached to them. Those are coral growths
like huge, old-fashoned fans, two or
three feet across but as thin and delicate
as a great piece of stiff lace. You can
break one off and swim up to the surface
with it quite easily. Then leave it on the
beach to dry out and bleach in the sun
(they smell awful until they are thor-
oughly dried out).

Down along the bottom of each coral
head there would be a swarm of little

The underwater world is often very beautiful but divers must be careful; it can also be dangerous

A good example of delicate, feathery sea fan coral

fishes from three to six inches long, of different shapes and colors. We tried to catch them with our hands but they were always too quick for us. They would let us get within a few feet of them but as soon as we put out a hand towards them, they would dart away, much faster than we could swim.

Here and there we would come across a starfish, usually about a foot across and yellowish-brown. And if we waited long enough, we could watch him walk. He goes so slowly that you hardly notice it at first, lifting one leg at a time and putting it down an inch or so farther forward, then doing the same with the others.

On the rocky patches, there is an occasional sponge and you will find lots of sea anemones which look like brownish flowers as big as your hand, with loose ends waving in the current. If you touch one with your finger, it shoots back very quickly indeed into a hard shell that is attached to the rock. In fact, we found that you need not actually touch them. They will do this if you put your finger about a quarter of an inch away from them, so they must be able to feel the water pressure as your finger gets close. Probably they withdraw as a defense against being eaten by fish. I never waited to see one come out again but it would be "flowering" the next time we passed that way.

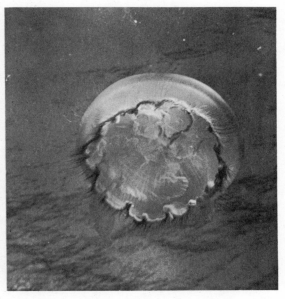

Sea basket sponge is in strange contrast   *to translucent jellyfish with frilled edges*

On one rocky patch, we found dozens of conchs. Those are shellfish eight or nine inches long that are good to eat. We took half a dozen back to the boat for supper (you steam them like clams) and kept the empty shells to use as horns. If you knock off the blunt end and blow it like a bugle, the conchshell makes a deep note that can be heard quite a long way.

The next day we got out the spear guns and spent the morning getting the hang of loading and firing them under water, before setting out for the reef, half a mile away. Moving along the surface and looking down, we passed over small hills and valleys in the bottom, with occasionally a dark and forbidding cave in the coral, deep down.

Then we came to the reef. A steep, craggy cliff rising up out of the deep, its water was dark almost to the surface.

This is a fish, not a plant! The basket starfish curls its tentacles to bring food to its mouth which is underneath

43

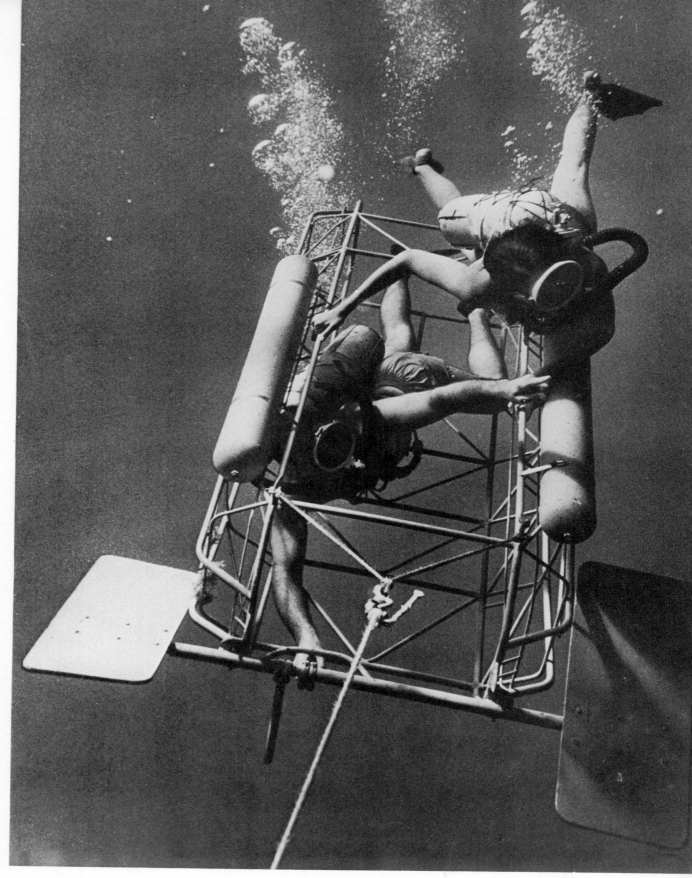

This rig serves as an underwater tow for skin divers. A boat on the surface pulls it along

All down the side of it were jagged rocks and dark holes, with sea fans, weed and sea anemones growing in all the crevices. The water surged to and fro across the top of it, and down the side of it there were fish feeding. At one time you could see as many as three or four fish from ten to 15 pounds, and a whole mess of little ones.

Spearing one of the larger fellows is more like hunting than fishing. You work your way in behind a fish that is moving slowly away from you, taking care to stay opposite the sun, so that your shadow won't frighten him. Then, when you are close enough, you dive to his level, take aim and fire.

You only get one shot. The moment he realizes that you are after him, he flicks his tail and is gone. But fish seem to be slow thinkers, for there is usually a pause of a second or so after he notices you before he swims away. That is where you get your chance.

If, like us, you never shoot more than you intend to eat, the next problem is to get your fish back to the boat. We do that by towing it at the end of the nylon line. We swim back with the gun, and let the fish follow with the spear. The reason for that is that a barracuda may smell the blood from your fish and come rushing in to grab it. If he does, you do not want to be in the way. It is far better to lose a fish than to tangle with a barra-

The snorkel lets you breath with your face under water. If you go too deep, a ball in the tube will rise and stop water coming in

cuda, especially when your gun is unloaded.

tricks are risks of the underwater trade

Apart from fish and conchs, we found plenty of big lobsters in the Tobago Cays. (Technically, in that area these are crayfish but everyone calls them lobsters.) There is a trick to catching them. You swim along until you find a hole a foot or two across under a coral head or a rock, right on the sea floor. Then, if you look closely, you may see a pair of long, thin black feelers sticking out of the hole, waving slowly from side to side. That is a lobster. To catch it, you swim down to the bottom and pry it out of the hole with your spear.

There are usually three or four lobsters in one hole, so you take all but one back to the boat. You let the last lobster loose on the sea bottom and push it around with your spear to make it move, but you don't let it go to its hole. After

45

Flying fish are named for their gliding leaps above water

a few moments, it will take off across the bottom and lead you to the next hole, where you will find three or four more lobsters. You will go on this way until you have as many as you need.

We met one group of skin divers who hunt fish in the inland rivers of Jamaica. They go off in canoes down the narrow rivers that wind through the dense mangrove swamps, and often, with nothing but the basic skin diving gear, they will swim far under the banks through the tangled mangrove roots to where the fish are.

To add to the risk, those rivers are full of crocodiles. Just before we got there, one man was bitten on the left hand by a four-foot crocodile, so he reached for his knife with his right

hand and the crocodile bit that one, too. Fortunately it was a small crocodile and he recovered. But I have seen one over eight feet long in those waters, and the largest one caught there was 13 feet long and weighed half a ton. Unlike the comparatively safe alligators, crocodiles are mean creatures that will attack whenever they get the chance.

more equipment

You can see a good deal under the water from a glass-bottomed boat, that is, a small boat 20 to 30 feet long with a flat bottom. In the middle, there is an oblong well some six feet long with a sheet of strong glass in the bottom of it. The sides of the well are high enough so that, if the glass should get broken, the boat won't sink. Usually seats are placed all around the well, facing inward toward it, and a canopy is stretched overhead to keep the sun off. Such a rig is powered by one or two outboard motors.

A useful thing that you can make yourself is a glass-bottomed box. This is a watertight wooden box about a foot square with a sheet of quarter-inch plate glass in the bottom of it and a handle on each side to hold it by.

If you kneel in a small boat with your head over the side and hold the box in front of you in the water, you can see almost as well as you would with a mask on and your head under water. This box

The least touch of fire coral feels like a painful burn on skin

The modern aqualung, with its portable air tanks strapped securely to explorer's back and out of

way of his hands and feet, allows skin diver to swim about with much of the watery freedom of a fish

61 11341

Man's view of objects beneath waters' surface is conditioned by an angle of refraction of light. Diagram shows how direct vision is deflected

is very useful for looking for things on the bottom in cold weather when you would not want to stay under water for long. So long as you keep the sun off the glass (a big shade hat is good for this), you can make photographs through this contraption with great success.

Another way to take underwater photographs from above is by using a Polaroid filter on your camera. Provided you keep the handle on it pointed towards the sun, this colorless filter will cut out nearly all the reflections on the surface, so that you can make pictures straight through it.

If you want to take photographs under the water, there are all kinds of cameras made for the job or, depending on what you want and how much you can afford to spend, you can get a case to put your ordinary camera in.

The simplest and cheapest rig is a soft plastic case with a glass window in it that you can use on any kind of camera. This will work quite well down to 15 or 20 feet and you simply grip the knobs on the camera through the soft plastic. The plastic is usually clear so that you can see what you are doing. This kind of case will also work for a light meter in shallow water.

Then there are medium-priced cameras that are made especially for underwater work. These are water-tight and

For undersea photography, camera is covered by watertight case

Fish's eye view is also conditioned by surface refraction. Sun can be glimpsed only straight overhead. Other views are angled

have controls much the same as those on an ordinary camera. Some of them also have flash attachments built to work under water, which are handy even at shallow depths where the water is muddy and it is quite dark.

You can also get special water-tight casings for any kind of still or movie camera, but they are rather expensive. Finally there are the specially built underwater cameras and lighting systems right up to full-size professional motion-picture rigs; those, however, are very expensive indeed.

There is one gadget that will let you stay down in shallow water for as long as you want and that you can make yourself. It consists of about 20 or 30 feet of plastic hose with a float on one end, so that this end sticks well out of the water. You swim down, breathing in through the bottom end of the hose which you hold in your mouth. You breathe out through your nose, as the float follows you along on the surface. We use such a rig sometimes for cleaning the bottoms of boats in out-of-the-way places where we cannot get an Aqualung. As a matter of fact it is a very old idea, as you can see from drawings of the 15th century, but it still works quite well. You must breathe out through your nose, though. Otherwise you simply get your own stale breath going up and down the tube.

Spearing fish is tricky; if they see your shadow, they run

off shore | 4

You may be suprised to know how much is going on under the water close to home. If you live near a river, canal, or harbor, look down and generally all you will see is dark, muddy, swirling water. But underneath the surface, hidden in the murk, are all sorts of things for you to see and hear.

If you put your head under the water in a busy harbor and listen, you will hear the deep, loud "thump, thump" of ships' propellors, and the high-pitched, musical whirring of the high-speed ones belonging to small boats.

Then you may catch the steady "ping" of a ship's echo sounder, the eerie clank of chains, and an occasional loud rattle and thud. The chains that clank are holding navigation buoys in place against the current, and the rattle and thud are the rattling of a ship's anchor chain and the great thud when the anchor lands on the bottom.

buoys

Sometimes, instead of anchoring, a ship will make fast to a mooring buoy.

This is a little more trouble but it is much stronger than any anchor that she could carry and it is fine if she has to wait around when there are strong winds and currents.

A Mooring Buoy is a round, flat thing that floats on the water. Underneath it, there is a heavy chain that goes straight down and then splits into two (or sometimes three) "legs" that snake along the bottom in different directions for several yards. On the end of each leg there is a big, heavy "mushroom" anchor, that looks just like a big iron mushroom. The top of the buoy is flat, so that a man can stand on it and fasten the ship's chain to a big ring in the middle. Then the ship is all set, securely hooked on to a massive rig that will hold her in almost any weather.

In other places, you will see the same kind of buoy, but with a pipe sticking up on top of it. That is a fueling buoy. It is like a mooring buoy except that it has a flexible pipe running from it along the bottom to the shore. A ship can make fast to it, then hook up a pipe to it and

Three types of marker,
buoys to indicate left and
right of channels, and a
mooring buoy with two
anchors for minimum shift

A new anchor buoy is launched to mark a navigation channel.
This one has a flashing light (top) and clanging bell (below)

get fuel from tanks on land. This is very useful where it is too shallow for large ships to get to a dock.

Other buoys you see in a harbor are navigation buoys. They come in many shapes and sizes and each one is marked on the charts, so that you can tell exactly where you are and where you can safely go.

The smallest kind of markers are spar buoys. Those are just straight pieces of wood, about the size of telephone poles, anchored in the water. They are usually painted with black and white stripes and the chains that hold them keep them more or less upright. But whenever there is any current they lean over, which makes them useful for seeing what the current is up to if you are boating or skin diving.

Then there are nun and can buoys. Those are used to mark the two sides of a channel. The nuns are red and have pointed tops, while the cans are black and have square tops, so that you can still tell which are which, even if the light is bad. They are much bigger than they look, each has more under water than shows above the surface.

Lastly there are the big buoys that mark the important channels and corners. They have flashing lights on them (red, white, or green) and often bells, whistles or gongs as well, so that you can recognize them in a fog. Out of the

water, one of these looks about the size of a city bus, stood on end. On top, it has the light, then a ring to protect that, then a steel framework. Inside the frame is the bell, with four clappers that bang against the sides as the buoy rocks on the waves. Lower down, you can see two hatches where the batteries are put that run the light. And under the water there is a big weight to keep the buoy right side up, then a chain that goes down to an anchor on the bottom.

Other things you will find on the bottom of a harbor are cables, usually electric or telephone cables, marked on the shore by signs saying: "Do Not Anchor."

Sometimes too there are wires or chains, on which cable ferries pull themselves across the harbor. These are big, flat barges with an engine but no propellor. They take aboard a load of cars and then crank up the engine which pulls the cable out of the water ahead of them and drops it back in behind them. So they go across to the other side, like a huge, noisy spider.

beyond the harbors

As you go out into the deeper water beyond our harbors, the first things you see are fishing boats of all shapes and sizes chuffing busily around. On the surface, they look much like any other boats, except for the tangle of gear on their decks. But beneath the waves they are doing strange things in the hope of catching fish.

Some are using seines, which are long, narrow nets that hang up and down in the water; floats keep one side up and weights keep the other side down. The fishermen put them out in a great circle, fencing in all the fish in that patch of sea. Then they pull the nets in, closing the circle, and drag the whole mess of nets and fish onto their boats.

Other boats may be using beam trawls. These are great sack-shaped nets with wooden beams to keep their mouths open, which the men drag along the bottom, scooping up any fish that get in their path. And the little boats are probably out after lobsters, putting down pots to catch them or pulling them up for a check.

A lobster pot is really a cunning trap. It is a frame crate covered with wire mesh, with just one way in, through a tunnel at one end. Inside is a piece of bait. The lobster sees the bait and tries to get in to eat it. This must take him some time, for lobsters are not very bright. But finally he finds the tunnel and crawls through it into the pot. Then the stupid creature can't find his way out again, and so he is there waiting for you when you come back.

Lobster pots are a problem for people in small boats. Near the coast the floats are all over the sea, and if you get one

These herring fishermen use beam trawl, a sack-shaped net, to haul their catch

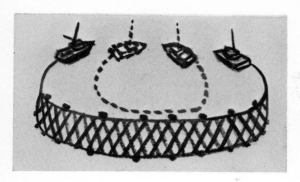

*Seines are nets weighted
on the bottom, with floats of
cork at top. They hang down
in water and trap fish when
drawn together before raising*

of the lines around your propellor, it is a job to get it off. But you find these only in rocky areas. In other places you find fish traps, which are worse.

A fish trap is a long line of wooden poles, sticking way up out of the water and stretching for a mile or more out to seaward. Between the poles there are nets, and if you run into that lot on a dark night, you will spend some time working your way free. But the idea is to catch fish, after all, not little boats.

The fish come swimming along the shore until they see the nets. Then they turn out to seaward and swim along beside them, looking for a way around the end. But at the end there is a pound, and in the pound there is a big net lying flat on the bottom. When the pound is full of fish, the fishermen lift the net. And there they are, caught.

The latest way to catch fish on a big scale is by electricity. This is very new, but it may well be the way fishing boats of the future will work. For some reason, if you lower two coils of wire into the sea and send an electric current from one to the other, all the fish in between promptly turn and swim toward one of the coils. So you swap that coil for a big funnel with a pipe leading up to the boat and a pump to suck up the water. This works like a charm. The fish swim right into the funnel, get pumped up with the water, and land on the deck,

all ready for sorting and packing. You do need a full size ship to carry the generators and the big pumps, which explains why not so many fishermen have adopted this method yet.

lightships and lighthouses

Sooner or later, as you sail along the coast, you will come to a lightship. This is a big, steel boat anchored out at sea as a seamark for ships—a sort of de luxe navigation buoy. It is painted red, with its name on the side, and it has, besides a light, a fog horn and a radio direction-finding station. Often, under the water, it also has a gadget like an echo sounder that sends out a "ping" at the same time as the "pip" on the radio.

Now, the radio direction finder gives a ship the direction of the station but not the distance. But the radio signal is received in almost no time at all (it travels 186,000 miles a second) and the sound signal, in water, goes at 4,945 feet a second. So, by measuring the time between the "pip" and the "ping," you can figure how far you are from the station. By this calculation, you know exactly where you are.

Each lightship has a crew of men living aboard her to look after the boat and her equipment. That may sound like a dull job, but in a gale or fog it is anything but dull. I have sailed past the Am-

The lightship is a big steel boat anchored offshore as a sea marker—a sort of king-size navigation buoy

brose Lightship, just outside New York harbor, in a gale and seen that great, heavy boat leap like a fish, showing fully a third of her keel clear out of the water. We were in port a couple of hours later, but those men had to stay out there and take it all day and night.

Actually, their greatest danger is being run down by other ships in a fog. Vessels will aim straight at a lightship (though they are not supposed to), using their radio direction finders to take them up to it.

Now and then, one makes a perfect shot and hits it. The Ambrose Lightship was rammed this past summer.

Imagine what it is like to be aboard a lightship in a fog, heaving on the swell, with water dripping off everything and nothing in sight, whichever way you look, but a blank wall of gray mist. All around you, hidden in the fog, great ships go rumbling and splashing by, any one of them big enough to crush you like a beetle. Every few seconds, there is a thundering roar as your fog horn sounds off, so loud that you can hardly hear yourself think. And you always know that, out there in the murk, some joker may be aiming straight at you.

A lighthouse is a much better deal for the men on it. It is firmly set in the bottom of the sea and does not rock, for one thing. It is usually in such shallow water that a ship couldn't hit it if she

Many a sailor's eyes have scanned fog and storm for the friendly flash of the lightship's beacon

tried. She would run aground first. And it has rocks piled around it, under the water, to make sure it stays put—a fact worth remembering if you get close.

oil beneath the sea

A thing that looks rather like a light-house, only bigger, is an offshore drilling rig. This is a great platform, set on long piles out in the middle of nowhere, with huts and an oil drilling rig on it. The operators drill straight down through the bottom of the sea for thousands of feet, until they come to a pool of oil. Then they pump it out, just as they would on land, and send it ashore by pipeline or in barges.

Mostly you find these in the Gulf of Mexico, but you may find one anywhere on the continental shelf, and they are apt to give you quite a surprise at night in a small boat. You are sailing along on the open sea when suddenly you come on a whole mess of lights that are all wrong for a ship and make no sense at all until you realize what they are.

This lighthouse has guided fishermen safely back to Gloucester, Mass., for 100 years

research boats

Another thing that can give you a bit of a jolt is a research ship letting off depth charges. You see her and think she is just another small ship until there comes a loud roar and a column of water shoots up into the air behind her. The crew is sounding the depth of mud on the bottom of the sea.

Often, in fairly shallow water, there will be a layer of mud on the bottom, with solid rock farther down. So they let off a depth charge that makes a loud ex-plosion just under the water. The sound goes down to the mud, and part of it comes straight back up to the ship's receiving gear. But the rest goes on down, through the mud, and bounces back off the rock below it. Since the part that goes all the way down has farther to go, it takes longer to get back. So they get two echoes. By figuring the depth of each and computing the difference, they can tell how thick the mud is, and one more fact is added to our small store of knowledge of the world we cannot see.

61

the dangerous deep | 5

Exactly what lives in the depths of the great oceans nobody knows for sure. Whales and sharks, octopi and squid we know about. But how about sea serpents? There was a time when gigantic serpents, 60 and 70 feet long, roamed the seas. They lived in the depths and only came up to the surface now and then. This much we do know. But are they still around? Perhaps.

Not long ago, a destroyer of the U. S. Navy sighted something in the Atlantic Ocean. It was about 100 feet long and three feet across, and it was moving along on the surface with a snakelike motion. At least two of the ship's officers saw it, and when they rammed it they saw blood in the water. Then it disappeared from sight.

That could easily have been a sea serpent. Or it might have been a giant ribbonfish, that is, a long, thin fish with a fin that runs along its back from its head all the way to its tail, giving it a very serpentine look. Ribbonfish 20 feet long have been found on the shore, and much larger ones have been sighted at sea, so

that there may well be 100-foot ones.

But if you want a real surprise, you only have to go swimming at night and bump into a ribbon worm (or nemertine). (You won't see them by the day, as they are asleep in the mud.) They look and behave much like ordinary worms, except that they swim around in the water at night, looking for food—and they happen to grow up to 90 feet in length. They won't hurt you, but still a 90 foot worm is quite something to meet on a dark night.

Or it might have been an extra-large anaconda. Anaconda are more like pythons, but they swim in the water and come in large sizes. There is the skin of an anaconda hanging on a wall in the Explorers' Club in New York City and it is 52 feet long.

We were once becalmed in my little sailboat for three days off the mouth of the Orinoco River (where there are known to be anacondas). Our deck was exactly 21 inches above the sea, and sitting there at night, alone on watch, wondering if a great snake would put its head out of the water and swallow me whole was not much fun at all.

squid

Quite a few stories of sea serpents have probably originated with people who have seen a giant squid cruising on the surface. With his great, bulbous head awash and his long tentacles trailing behind him, he would look like a serpent at a distance. And when it comes to giant squids, distance is something you can do with plenty of. I can't think of anything that I would less like to meet in a small boat or under the water.

A squid looks rather like an octopus, with long tentacles covered with suckers to grab his prey. But there the likeness ends. An octopus likes shallow water and a quiet life, hiding among the rocks and feeding on passing crabs. But a squid is a hunter by nature. And giant squids—they may be as much as 150 feet long—can really get around.

They are jet-propelled, complete with boosters. They are equipped for long distance navigation, and are the fastest things in the ocean. They propel themselves by drawing in water and squirting it out through a jet, which drives them forward like a rocket.

Squids have three hearts: one for the the head, which contains the navigation gear, and two more as "boosters" to keep their hugh motor muscles supplied with blood. Their eyes are exactly like humans' but they measure as much as three feet across, and they have great, parrot-like beaks to tear their prey apart.

Several giant squids 50 to 55 feet long have been caught and, from marks some of them have left on whales, we know that they may grow three times that big, or 150 to 165 feet. They live in the great depths (one was found tangled in a cable 3,240 feet down) and seldom come to the surface.

Their enemies are the great sperm whales, which normally feed on smaller squids. When a whale takes on a giant squid, a fierce battle starts. The whale has a huge, oil-filled buffer on the top of his head, and he tries to kill the squid by ramming it head on, at full speed, against a rock. The squid, on the other hand, knows that the whale can't breathe under water, so with some of his tentacles he grips his enemy and with the others hangs on to a rock, trying to hold the whale down until he drowns.

Both squids and octopi can send out a jet of black ink to confuse their enemies and deaden their sense of smell. Moray eels, which are vicious creatures, will often attack an octopus. But once the octopus has let off his ink, the eel can't find him without his sense of smell to guide him, even long after the ink has drifted away.

Divers avoid the stingray. With one lash of his sawtooth-edged tail he can injure a man

A couple of years ago, three of us were becalmed for five days in a 40-foot sailboat, in the middle of the Sargasso Sea, the famous wasteland of the ocean where sailing ships of old are said to have lain helpless until their crews died of thirst and the boats rotted and sank.

Today it is not quite so bad, because a modern sailboat will answer to the slightest puff of wind, and little by little you can work your way out of the Sargasso. But you have to be on watch all the time, day and night, alert to set your sails to the faintest breeze and gain a few more yards while it lasts.

Sitting there waiting, surrounded by the thick, yellow Sargasso weed, you wonder: about ships that have vanished without a trace; about the *Marie Celeste,* which was found in perfect order but without a soul aboard and no sign of why the crew had left; and about the monstrous creatures of the depths that can surface if they want to and would most likely do so in such a place.

On the third day, we were attacked by a shark. My wife, June, was on watch when suddenly we felt a bump. He hauled off for about 100 yards and came back at full speed, BUMP, into the boat. Each time he attacked he would turn over (his mouth was underneath, like most sharks), and, after a few times, his white underside was covered with smears of green paint from our bottom. But we had a good, strong boat, and he did her no harm. So he got mad and grabbed the rudder in his mouth, wrenching it to and fro. This made steering tiresome, so I took a great, long boathook and drove its sharp point as hard as I could into his head. The blow jarred my hand, as if I had struck a rock, but the shark left with a flourish

Did you know that whales breathe air, not water? If they stayed underwater too long they'd drown

There's no more frightening sight than watching tons of angry whale rushing toward your boat. His blowhole shows above water

and we never saw him again.

A shark has a brain the size of a golf ball and just about all the rest of him is muscle. So unless you hit that one tiny spot you may as well save your bullets, as far as killing him goes.

We were lucky, though, to be in a heavily built boat when the shark attacked us. If that had happened to my own little 20-footer, whose hull was less than half an inch thick, he would probably have come straight through the side. And a large, angry shark in a small cabin is a guest you don't really welcome.

The best way I know to get rid of a shark I learned from an old Chinese sea cook. You make a sandwich of two pieces of bread with a thick layer of hot English—or Chinese—mustard between. Throw this in the water ahead of your shark and he will promptly swallow it. Then he will leave—fast. I have never seen one come back after that treatment.

Altogether, I have met five different sharks under water at various times, and have never had any trouble with any of them. They have always gone

about their business and left me alone. However, I do know of cases where skin divers have been killed by sharks and, at one time during the last war when I was in Singapore, we lost over a hundred men in one year to sharks. The sharks in that area would attack a swimmer on sight, so you were supposed to swim inside shark fences made of heavy stakes. But a couple of times each week, someone would try swimming outside the fence and the sharks would get him. Usually a shark would bite a leg off and the man would die of shock.

They have the same trouble around Australia, yet in New Zealand (which is not so very far away) they have very little trouble with them. In the summer of 1960, sharks infested the waters off Long Island's beaches causing some damage and considerable alarm. It does not seem to be any one species of shark that attacks, so most probably it all depends on how much food they can find in any one place.

Most people I know who have met sharks in the water feel that they are a temperamental lot and not to be trusted. Most likely they will not attack, but they might so we don't take any chances. They bite more often at a swimmer's legs when his head is above water, so we always stay down and face a shark when we meet one. For the same reason, we never swim after dark in tropical waters when we can't see what we are doing. And if in doubt, we stay in shallow water close to the surf, where sharks hardly ever go.

A few natives of Barbados catch sharks (for the oil in their livers) from small boats. It takes three to man a boat. First, they row around until they find a shark sleeping. Then one man swims down with a rope with a noose on the end of it and slips the noose over the shark's tail. The man then swims back quickly to the boat and they all pull on the rope. The shark's tail is stiff and won't fold so, as soon as the noose draws tight, they've got it. The last step is to haul the shark up to the boat and kill it. There are very few men who want the job of going down with the rope, however, so that this isn't done very much.

Like most sharks, the one that attacked us in the Sargasso Sea had several pilot fish with him. There were two kinds, plain gray ones that swam ahead of him and striped ones that swam behind him. Pilot fish live on scraps of food left over when the shark kills some-

thing, and they seem to earn their keep by acting as lookouts and scouts for him.

But when I scared our shark off, the pilot fish all decided that we must be a bigger fish that had won a battle over him, so they let him go and stayed with us. For two days, they swam around us, the gray ones in a crescent ahead of us and the striped ones in line astern. Then a wind came up and the waves began to break and they went away.

One small striped one stayed with us a little longer but he kept getting rolled over by the breaking seas, until finally he decided it wasn't worth it and left us.

the barracuda

Barracudas are much smaller than sharks (I have never seen one more than five feet long) but they are probably more dangerous to a skin diver. For one thing, there are more of them, and they are quite big enough to kill you. For another, they are curious. Usually a shark will mind its own business but a barracuda will hang around often for fifteen minutes at a time, to see what you're doing.

He will stay just out of range of your gun (barracudas seem to have an instinct for this) and watch you, slowly opening his mouth to show you a fearsome set of triangular teeth, then snapping it shut again. If you move toward him, he moves back. If you move away,

This is everybody's Enemy Number One, the shark. He's hard to kill and harder to scare

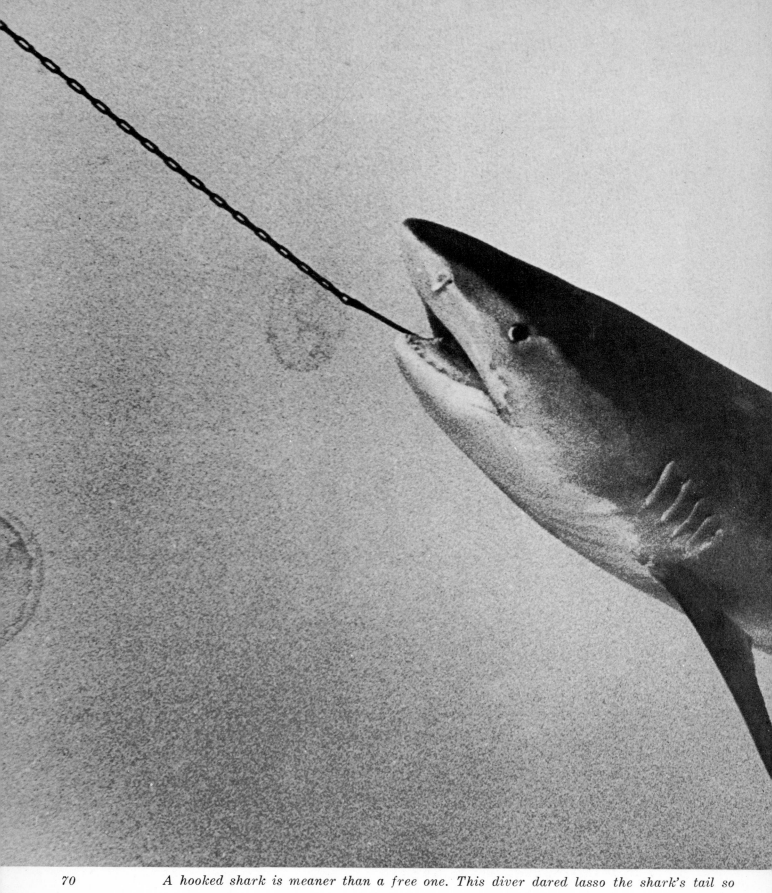

70   *A hooked shark is meaner than a free one. This diver dared lasso the shark's tail so*

that it could be brought aboard ship without fear of its powerful tail injuring someone

The moray eel likes dark caves but when it comes out, watch out! It can clamp its sharp teeth onto a man, wrap its tail around a rock and hang on until its victim has drowned

he moves forward. If you go down, he goes down, and so on. Then suddenly he will vanish.

Now the glass in your face mask is quite small, so that you can only see more or less straight in front of you. So you turn slowly around and there he is, behind you, watching, opening and shutting his mouth, and waiting.

Of course, like people, barracudas vary. I know a big old fellow that used to live under a boat in St. Thomas, in the Virgin Islands. He got plenty of scraps to eat from the yachts and was quite tame. In fact the local children would see him swimming by and jump off the dock on top of him, and he never seemed to mind.

The first time we met him, we didn't know about his reputation. We were in St. Thomas to fetch a 38-foot sailboat up to New York and had decided to clean the weeds off her bottom before we left, to make her go faster. I gave the mate a scrub brush and an aqualung, and asked him to go to it. For about an hour there were bubbles around the boat and we could see him moving about underneath us. Then he came up. The job was done. Of course, I asked him how he'd made out. "Fine" he said "except for that fool fish."

It turned out that the barracuda had keep sticking his nose over the mate's shoulder. And the mate, who knew nothing about barracudas, would hit him on the nose with the scrub brush. And so it had gone on, for an hour.

Another time we were anchored off Pigeon Island, in the Windward Islands, and I was ashore on the beach while a friend was skin diving along the shore. Suddenly he came out of the water faster than I have ever seen a man run before or since. It seems that five large barracudas had come sweeping across the bay in formation, looking very unfriendly indeed. Whether they would have attacked him I am not sure, but we found out that the natives never swam there in the late afternoons when the barracudas came by.

Many fish come by the same place, at the same time, every day. They have one place where they sleep and another where they feed, and they commute to and fro daily, like people.

eels

Two good reasons why we do not swim at night in tropical waters are fire coral and Moray eels. Fire coral looks much like other coral, but it is usually a bright orange or yellow and has a poison on it. If you brush against it, it will give you a bad sting that may even stun you.

Moray eels live in the dark caves and crevices in the coral. They don't come out much but, if you go too close to them, they will clamp their teeth down on you and hang on with their tails firmly wrapped around a rock until you

Looking innocent enough, moray eel pokes its snout out of rocks, alert for its prey

drown and they can eat you at their leisure. They are very tough and hard to kill—and they will not let go unless you kill them—so that they are probably the most dangerous thing a skin diver has to watch for under water.

Further north, in cooler waters, you find Conger eels in some rocky areas. They need watching, too, We saw a man who caught one from a small skiff one day. When we got there, the eel was writhing around in the boat, snapping its great jaws like a mad dog, and the fisherman—who had jumped over the side—was swimming around his boat, shouting for help.

All the eels that live in the creeks and rivers of America and Europe go to the Sargasso Sea to breed. And, mysteriously, the young find their way back to the very rivers and creeks their parents came from. How they do it, nobody knows. When eels get old, they leave their home waters and swim, often for thousands of miles, back to the Sargasso. Then they die.

fabulous fish

Not all fish can swim up from the depths the way a squid does. We know that there are some which explode if they swim too far up. They live in the deep waters and are built to stand the enormous pressure down there, but if they get up where the pressure is much less they can't take it, and they burst. So there may well be other creatures living down there that we have not learned of yet.

Sailing along at night on the open ocean, we have often seen lights under the water. They were maybe six feet down, about as bright as a 60-watt bulb, and kept flashing on and off. At first, we didn't believe our eyes, but later we got used to them. Probably they were deep-sea anglers or goosefish.

These are fearsome-looking fish that live in the inky darkness of the great depths, often going down 3,000 feet or more, and they have lights that they flash to attract other fish. The lights are on long rods that they wave in front of their huge mouths, and when the other fish come over to see what it is all about, they are swallowed whole. Goosefish four feet long have been caught, and they can swallow a fish almost as big as they are in one gulp.

A problem with night sailing in the tropics is flying fish. They are about nine inches long and look like herring but have long, thin, wings like a dragonfly's. They leap out of the water and can fly a hundred yards or more, 10 or 15 feet above the waves, before they fall back into the sea.

In the daytime they make a fine show, and the odd ones that hit your sails and

74

Not as large as a shark but big enough to kill a man, a barracuda looks like a torpedo and is just as dangerous. That sneering jawline covers a mouthful of needle-sharp teeth

fall on deck make good eating when fried in butter. But at night they are pests. You are sitting alone on watch, sleepily steering the boat as she eases her way over the swells in the gentle night breeze; all is peaceful and quiet when SPLAT, you get slapped in the stomach by a wet fish that drops onto the cockpit floor and flaps around with enough fuss to scare the life out of you.

These fish fly to get away from the big fellows that chase them, such as swordfish. We were looked over by a swordfish one day off the Dominican Republic. He was about five feet long, with a spike on his nose the size of a rolled umbrella, and he came skidding past us at high speed, standing on his tail, with his beady little eye following us as he went by. We were in my little boat and he could easily have thrust his sword through it, which would have made life quite exciting in the cabin, but luckily he didn't try.

whales and the playful porpoise

It must be even more impressive to run into a herd of narwhals, though. These are small Arctic whales, about 12 feet long; the males have thin, twisted horns about nine feet long on their heads, just like unicorns (in fact, this is where the legends of unicorns came from). Narwhals use their horns to fight and to break holes in the ice in order to breathe. Two or three thousand of them have been reported in a single herd—quite a thing to meet in a small boat.

We saw one fishingboat for sale cheap last year. We were sailing from Barbados to Bermuda in a 50-foot sailboat, and just as we came up to the harbor, we met a mad whale. He was about 70 feet long and must have weighed all of 70 tons, and he was jumping clear out of the water, landing with a great splash that shot up into the air like an exploding depth charge.

Our engine had broken down, so we sailed close along the rocky shore and slipped by him into the harbor. Maybe that was the best thing to do, for I don't think he noticed us moving silently along under sail. But he did see a small motor fishing boat and he turned it over, dumping the fisherman into the sea. The men got ashore, but the very next day there was an advertisement in the local paper saying: "Fishboat for Sale Cheap."

Other friends of ours once ran head on into a whale. They were sailing along in a small sailboat, near the Bahamas but still miles from land. The wife was down in the cabin when suddenly there was a great, jarring bump. She came flying on deck to see what had happened, thinking they must have hit a reef, and her husband, who was steering, greeted her with: "You know, I've never seen such big porpoises before."

They were in the middle of a school of small whales, each about as big as their boat, that were swimming around in circles, playing with them. For several minutes they sat, wondering what to do, as the monsters charged happily around them. Then suddenly the whales got bored with the game and swam off.

Often you do see real porpoises at sea. They swim so fast that they can play around the bow of the fastest ship, with plenty of speed to spare, and in the wartime convoys, more than one captain had a nasty scare from them. He would be on his bridge, looking out for submarines, when suddenly he would see something, that looked exactly like a torpedo, rushing through the water straight toward his ship. At the last second, it would swerve away and skim past his bow. Another porpoise.

We had one scare from them ourselves. We were approaching New York, out of St. Thomas, in a 40-foot sailboat and were becalmed in a thick fog. Just after dark we were on deck, listening for ships that might run us down before they saw us. Everything was still and dripping with damp from the fog; the boat heaved on the last of the swell and

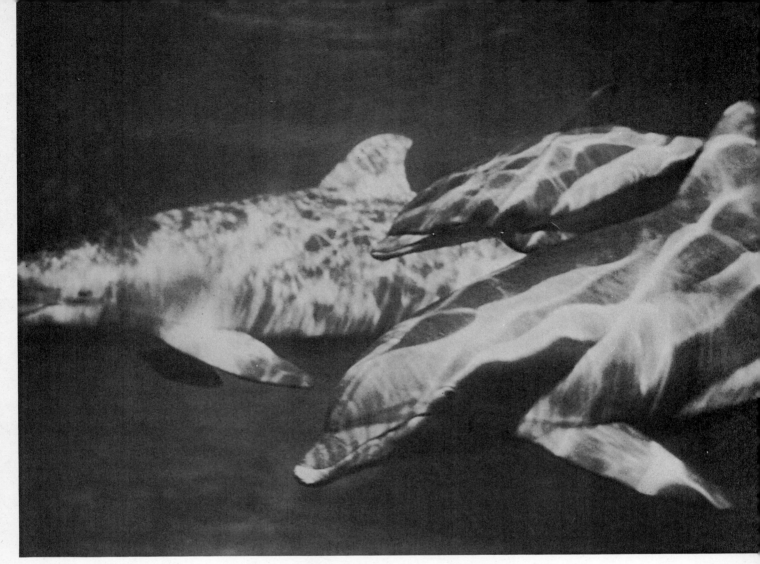

The porpoise may be smarter than people; it has the largest brain of any animal its size

we waited, listening.

Then, in the distance, we heard a faint hissing. Steadily it grew louder and came closer, sounding just like the bow wave of a ship. But where was the throb of her engines? Maybe the fog was playing tricks with the sound. It sometimes does. But still the noise came closer. We sounded our fog horn. No answer.

Soon the hissing noise was all around us. And we saw what it was—a huge school of porpoises, swimming along on the surface of the sea at high speed, jumping and playing as they went. With-

out a word, we went below and brewed up some strong, black coffee.

One reason why porpoises always seem to be playing is that they leap out of the water all the time. They do this because they are animals, not fish, and they must come up every minute or so to breathe. Whales are the same (though they can hold their breath longer), and they both smell exactly like cows if they come up to breathe close beside you.

But porpoises are a playful lot anyway. Maybe it is because they are very smart. Some scientists went to the

Face to face with an octopus, this diver came out alive even though his face mask was ripped off

Virgin Islands recently to try to find out how a porpoise manages to swim so fast (the navy would like to know how they do it). So far they haven't found that out, but they did discover that porpoises may be rather smarter than people. They have the biggest brains for their size of any animal, including man —which makes you think.

However, sometimes even the dumbest creatures can show you a trick or two. Not long ago, I was on a dock in Annapolis, Maryland. On the dock was a hut and in the hut was a tank of water, not connected to the sea in any way. And in the water were some oysters.

I asked someone which way the current was running. He looked at the oysters and said: "It's still running out." Puzzled, I asked him why he had looked at the oysters. And he said: "They know."

Oysters can't move around, so they must have their food brought to them. The current does that, but they only feed when it is running one way. So they open and shut when it changes. And those oysters, which had been in the tank for months, still knew exactly when it changed, though it does so at a different time each day.

There are also some pretty wild people around on the sea, even in these days. A few years ago, in Singapore, a group of us got hold of an old ship's lifeboat and rigged her as a ketch; I would often take her out by myself and go for a sail along the coast in my free time. Then I left, and sometime later I heard that shortly after I'd gone one of my Singapore friends had done the same thing. Only he had not come back. They found his body on the beach a few days afterwards. Pirates had killed him for his watch and the money he had on him.

If you are going up the Red Sea toward the Suez Canal in a small boat, you need a machine gun and a supply of hand grenades aboard, for the pirates there all have rifles, and unless you are better armed than they, you are not likely to get through alive.

I have even been shot at in the Caribbean quite recently. Two of us were sailing past the island of St. Vincent in my 20-foot sailboat one dark night, and we noticed a light on the shore. Thinking nothing of it, we went on tacking in toward the coast, until we heard the whine of rifle bullets overhead.

We looked out to seaward, and against the clear, starry sky, we could make out the sails of a big schooner standing in toward the land, with no lights. Clearly she was doing a bit of smuggling, and the boys on shore were advising us to get lost. So we doused our lights and made a couple of quick tacks out to seaward without further delay. We can take a gentle hint.

the unknown world 6

For well over 2,000 years men have been working under the sea. Aristotle, the Greek philosopher, described an elephant's trunk as looking like the tubes used by divers for breathing under water, as if they were ordinary things that everybody knew about in 340 B. C.

A modern diving suit is made of waterproofed canvas, with tight rubber bands around your wrists and ankles, and looks like a suit of long underwear that somebody has starched. After a diver struggles into it, he puts on the weighted boots and belt that will keep him down on the bottom. Then his assistant bolts on his helmet and he's all ready to go.

Usually divers work from a boat and an assistant helps the diver over the side, down a short ladder and into the water. Then he drifts down to the bottom, while the man on board pays out his air hose and life line. The whole rig is very heavy and awkward, after skin diving, and one wonders how anybody can work in such a thing.

It is amazing what the divers can do, though. Not long ago, we were in Bermuda when the cruise ship, *Reina del Pacifico*, went aground in the harbor there. She ran off the channel at a corner and plowed her way into the soft coral, pushing it up on either side of her so that, at low tide, people could stand knee-deep in the water and touch the side of the ship.

She went aground at high water, two days before spring tides, so that if she did not get off at once, she would be there for a month. The most powerful tugboats in the harbor could not even budge her, as she was firmly wedged in the coral: a nice, tight, snug fit. It looked like a hopeless case. Then the divers came along.

They anchored their boats beside the ship and got out a gadget that looks like a fire hose, with a big pump on the boat and a nozzle on the far end. It puts out a jet of water so powerful that it washes away coral the way a garden hose will wash away sand. But if a diver used a single jet like that under water, he would go rushing off backwards like a squid in a hurry. So it has two jets, one facing each way, that balance each other.

Using a periscope, the submarine captain can see what's happening on the surface

The divers went down beside the ship and started boring a tunnel through the coral with the jet, clear underneath her. That must have been a nerve-wracking job. Imagine crawling along in a narrow, dark tunnel under the sea with a great ship on top of you, well knowing that she has only to settle a little to trap you beneath her!

But they made it through to the other side. Then they went through again from side to side, dragging a steel cable under the ship. And after that they bored another tunnel, and another, until they had placed several cables under the ship. Then, at low tide, they attached the ends of the cables to floats. As the tide came in, the floats rose up and lifted the ship enough for the tugs to get her off.

the divers' enemies

Sometimes divers have trouble with sharks but their real enemies are giant clams, pressure, and currents. The giant clams are like ordinary clams but about four feet across and, if you have ever tried to open an oyster, you can imagine how powerful they are. Often they will sit around with their shells open but, if a diver steps into one, the clam promptly clamps shut on his foot. It doesn't mean any harm but it has a grip like a steel

In a flash of foam the U.S.S. Shark surfaces after a dive. Modern as the idea of the submarine may seem, history tells that America used one against the British in 1776

vise and our diver can't get out. Unless he can break the thick, tough shell, he is stuck there, firmly anchored to the bottom of the sea.

Water pressure, the same as the stopping up a swimmer feels in his ears when he dives, has always been a problem for divers. If you go down too deep, the pressure of the water makes the nitrogen in your blood come bubbling out into your blood stream, to poison you. When that happens, you get what Jacques Cousteau (inventor of the Aqualung) calls "rapture of the deep". You never know it is coming on and you can't even be sure when you've got it,

but suddenly you feel as if nothing mattered and you begin to do stupid things. One skin diver took his air tube out of his mouth and offered it to a passing fish. Unless your companions take over quickly and get you up to a higher level, you are about to drown.

For that reason alone, 300 feet is about as far as a diver dare go down, and he cannot do any heavy work much below 150 feet. However, people are already working on equipment to enable us to go deeper. If they succeed, one of the world's last frontiers will have been pushed back a little farther.

The divers' worst enemy of all is the

A diver gets set to go underwater on a lowering platform

force of sudden, deep-water currents that they run into from time to time. Without warning, a great gust of water will swirl about you and sweep you off your feet. When that happens you may bang your head against a rock, or lose part of your gear.

There is a group of skin divers called SOGETRAM (for "Société Generale de Travaux Maritimes et Fluviaux") that started in France in 1952 and now has offices in several countries. They have been doing all kinds of underwater work on dams, piers, ships and so on with great success. The only man they ever lost was caught by a sudden underwater current.

They have a training school for their divers and one part of the final exam there is to build a wooden box under water. You are given the wood, a saw, a hammer and some nails, and down you go to the bottom. Then you start building your box. But every time you let a bit of wood go, it rushes up to the surface and each time you put down your hammer it is liable to disappear into the mud. It must be one of the most frustrating jobs you can think of. But it is typical of a diver's work, for not only does he have a job of work to do but he also has to cope with the problems of doing it under water.

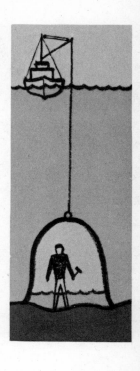

Diving bell has air pumped in to upper portion to keep water near lower part of 'cup' so that diver works in near-dry conditions

the diving bell

One way out is to use a diving bell. It was invented by Roger Bacon in 1250, and Augustus Siebe developed it into a practical rig, building several of them around 1820.

If you hold an ordinary glass upside down and put it in a basin of water, you can see that the water only rises half an inch or so inside it, leaving the rest of the glass full of air. This is because, as the water comes in, its force compresses the air until the air pressure builds enough resistance to stop the water from rising any farther.

Enlarging on this principle, you take a big glass bell with a ring on top to lift it by, and you lower it by crane to the bottom of the sea.

But there is a drawback: The deeper you go, the higher the water comes up inside the bell. So you rig an air hose from your boat and pump air down into the bell to push the water out. Then you can stay more or less dry and work in comfort. But you still have a pressure problem since the air pressure must be maintained at the same level as that in the water outside. This prevents your going any deeper than a diver can. However these bells are very useful for many jobs, especially for getting men out of a damaged submarine, as you can lower one down on top of her and work right on the hull. In fact the navy has special ones, built for that purpose.

submarines

Submarines have been around for a long time, too. The first one to be used in warfare was the American *Turtle* that attacked the British fleet in New York Harbor in 1776. She was shaped like an egg standing on end and held one man, who turned her propellor by hand from the inside. She could go down to 18 feet but she was very slow and had quite a time escaping the rowboats that were sent out to catch her.

Then, 110 years later, the Swedish designer Nordenfelt built a steam-driven one that could go for 16 miles at five knots and dive to 30 feet. But she could only stay down for five minutes at a time. Submarines were not taken seriously until World War I, when German U-boats started sinking ships in a big way.

The U-boats were driven under water by electric motors that ran off batteries, and diesel engines charged the batteries. The diesels could only be run on the surface, however, as they needed lots of air, so the subs had to surface every night in order to run in the daytime. But they could stay down all day and make about 12 knots under water if they had to. With a good supply of torpedoes, they were a real menace.

A torpedo is like a baby submarine,

In order to work on the ocean floor, divers must wear weighted boots and belts to hold them down

This is the dark world that divers see. The fish are scup; they live 500 feet down in the Gulf of Mexico

with a motor that runs off compressed air and a charge of explosive in its nose. It can make 40 knots or better but it can't go very far, so that the sub has to get quite close before she fires it. In World War I, you had to aim the whole sub at your target, fire your torpedo and hope you would hit it. But now there are torpedoes that pick up the sound of a ship's propellors and aim themselves at them; with one of those, you can hardly miss.

To see where she is going, a submarine has a periscope. That is a long tube that sticks straight up above the water when she is near the surface. Inside it are lenses like those in a telescope and the ends are bent over (with prisms to bend the light) so that the captain can look in his end to see what is going on above the water's surface.

In World War II, the German Navy developed the snorkel. That is a breathing tube for engines that allows you to run your diesels while you stay just below the surface so that you can go faster and keep your batteries charged for deep diving.

Then along came the American atomic submarines that made all the others look like toys. An atomic submarine can dive so deep that no surface ship can find her. She can run so fast that no ship can catch her. And she can stay down for as long as she wants to. The *Nautilus* sailed clear across the Arctic Ocean, under the ice, to Europe. The *Skate* broke through the ice and came up at the North Pole. The *Triton* sailed right around the world in 61 days without surfacing.

But the *George Washington* is the one to watch. She carries 16 Polaris rockets with nuclear warheads and has shown that she can fire them from under the water. So now we have a ship that nobody can catch or even find, that can go anywhere in the world at high speed and deliver a devastating nuclear attack.

Already the Navy is building more like her and, with several of them roaming the oceans, unseen and unheard, no nation is likely to start a war. It just wouldn't be worth trying. While an enemy might hope to wipe out our rocket bases on land in the first attack, they would still have to reckon with those submarines, hidden in the depths of the oceans, waiting to reply with terrible effect. And so, from a weapon of war, has come a great living hope of peace.

87

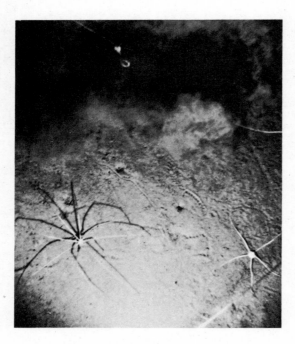

Pictures of ocean floor show (top) a sea spider, three brittlestars and strange tracks. Thought to be manganese ore (below), lumps were photographed 3 miles down

what does the future hold?

Now for the future. What do the oceans hold for us? We still do not know for sure but we are working on it. This year the United States spent $55,000,-000 on undersea research and will probably be spending twice that much within a couple of years. But we are getting results. Already man has been down to the deepest place in the world.

This year Professor Piccard's bathyscaph, *Trieste*, crewed by his son, Jacques, and Lieutenant Don Walsh of the United States Navy, touched the bottom of the ocean in Challenger Deep, the deepest part of the Marianas Trench, 35,800 feet below the surface.

A bathyscaph is a special craft built for deep-water diving. It floats under the water the way a balloon floats in the air, with tanks of gasoline (which is lighter than water) to keep it up and hoppers of iron shot for ballast. The pressure of the water does not bother it, since the tanks are open to the sea and the water can flow freely in and out of them.

But the crew ride in a sphere slung underneath this balloon, which must stand up to the terrific weight of water above it. At the bottom, its door alone has 3,000 tons of water pressing on it, while the total weight on the sphere is equal to that of five battleships.

Professor Piccard figured that down

In this bathyscaph, the Trieste, Jacques Piccard and Lt. Don Walsh of the U.S. Navy went down to a depth of 35,800 feet in the deepest part of the Marianas Trench in the Pacific

there a hole in the sphere the size of a pinhead would let in a jet of water that would go straight through a man like a bullet and fill up the whole cabin in a few seconds. So the door had better be a nice tight fit.

The *Trieste* was well tested before she started down. Already she had made 64 dives to lesser depths and behaved well. And now Jacques Piccard meant to show that she could go to the deepest place in the world before he handed her over to Lieutenant Walsh, who will run her for the Navy.

It was a rough day in the Pacific Ocean, about 200 miles off Guam, when the dive started. The Navy tugboat,

Wandank, and the destroyer escort, *Lewis*, were rolling and pitching as they marked out the exact spot where the *Trieste* would start her dive.

Cramped in the tiny sphere, barely six feet across, Piccard and Walsh checked the electrical circuits by which they could release gas or ballast, checked their instruments, checked their gear. Then they gave the okay. Mechanic Giuseppe Buono closed the door from the outside, Piccard released a little gas, and the *Trieste* started down.

At 300 feet she came to the thermocline (a layer of cold water), and stopped. Piccard released more gas and started moving again, down into the

The pilot and copilot sit in the sphere beneath the body of the bathyscaph. Gasoline is carried in the tank above

stillness of the depths, at the speed of an old-fashioned elevator. By 1,500 feet they were in total darkness, sliding through a black void to the unknown.

By 5,600 feet they put in a phone call to the surface. It came through loud and clear on the sonic telephone (an instrument that uses sound waves in the water). Up there, the ships were bouncing in a rising sea. But over a mile below them the *Trieste* hung, silent and still, as she went steadily deeper.

They called again at 10,000 feet and then at 13,000 feet. But the voice above them was getting weak. They must be getting out of range of the telephone. They hung up. They were on their own.

At 20,000 feet they saw luminous trails in the water. What made them? We don't know yet. Did anything live down there? No one knew. If some-

thing did, it would probably stay away from them, so that they would not see it anyway. Unless it attacked them.

At 32,500 feet they felt a sudden shock and heard a dull cracking sound. They couldn't have hit the bottom, for it had not even shown up on their echo sounder yet. They checked the sphere. It seemed to be all right. Their instruments showed nothing unusual. So on they went, down towards the bottom.

Then they picked up the same noise on the echo sounder. Piccard released ballast and the *Trieste* slowed down, but kept on going. They turned on their outside lights. Nothing below them. Then something white. The ocean floor.

Gently Piccard eased her down and she settled on a carpet of soft ooze, the color of ivory. They were on the bottom of the ocean. And there, in front of their porthole, a fish swam by, taking no notice of them. It looked like a sole and was about a foot long, and it was obviously very much alive down there.

That meant two things: It meant that creatures could live in those depths. And it meant that there must be currents to take oxygen down to them. A whole new world of exploration had been opened up. It may take us many years to find out all the secrets of the deep oceans, but Piccard and Walsh have proved that man can go down there. And they have shown us how to do it.

The last bubbles of air rush to the surface from the conning tower as the bathyscaph starts its dive

PATRICK ELLAM

Born in London in 1920, Patrick Ellam started sailing at the age of two. By 18, he had crossed the English Channel alone many times in small sailboats. He went to school in England, France and Germany and, at 19, joined the Royal Artillery. Later, during World War II, he volunteered into a Special Operations group and worked with the French underground.

In September, 1951, Ellam with one friend as crew sailed from England in a sloop less than 20 feet long, with no engine, called *Sopranino*. Their purpose was a year-long test cruise to Spain, Portugal, Africa, the Canary Islands and thence across the Atlantic to the United States via the West Indies. The experience was to prove that extremely light, small sailing craft could negotiate the great waters.

Patrick Ellam published an account of this experimental crossing in 1953, in a book named for the craft, *Sopranino* (Norton). The next assignment Ellam undertook was for *Sports Illustrated* for which he worked for six months in the West Indies. In 1956, he published *The Sportsman's Guide to the Caribbean* (Barnes). This unusual guide covers everything from an alligator hunt to fights between a poisonous snake and a mongoose!

In 1955, Patrick Ellam, who had married and become an American citizen, started a yacht delivery service, sailing yachts from port to port as they were bought and sold. He now has four teams moving small boats of all kinds over an area ranging from Canada to South America. He also directs a small-boat design and consultant service.

His first underwater experience was obtained during World War II. Since then, Ellam has been pursuing underwater exploration and, incidentally, spear fishing as a hobby.

195195